THE GREAT BRIDGE

THE GREAT BRIDGE

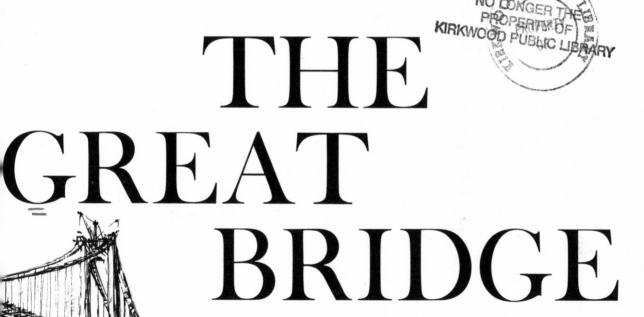

The Verrazano-Narrows Bridge

DRAWINGS BY LILI RÉTHI, F. R. S. A.

Text by Edward M. Young

ARIEL/FARRAR, STRAUS & GIROUX, *New York*

Foreword

BY ROBERT MOSES, *Chairman*
Triborough Bridge and Tunnel Authority

The Verrazano-Narrows Bridge is a structure of superlatives, a creation of usefulness, imagination, superb engineering and fine architecture. It will dominate the world's greatest harbor.

In its name this span links the Old World and the New.

The bridge is much more than the world's highest suspended water crossing. It is a link to the future—a future that holds the promise of at least a substantial part of a solution of the metropolitan traffic problem. This bridge with its immense approaches bypasses Manhattan and the city core and makes outlying areas accessible. It is the most important link in the great highway system stretching from Boston to Washington or, if you please, Maine to Florida.

Preface

BY OTHMAR H. AMMANN

The engineering phase in the construction of a great bridge such as the Verrazano-Narrows Bridge in New York, is essentially the application of scientific and technological progress in many fields. Modern construction of a large bridge is a complex process, involving intricate calculations and geometrics, now vastly aided by electronic machines, more efficient production of materials in mines and quarries, fabrication in mills and shops, transportation to storage places and to the site, and finally the assembly and erection of the various parts at the site.

In her collection of sketches of some of the construction processes in the building of the largest suspension bridge so far built, Lili Réthi has admirably succeeded in giving a realistic pictorial presentation of major construction operations, such as the sinking of the deep tower caissons, the assembling of the towers to a height of nearly 700 feet, the spinning of the huge cables, and the assembling of the deck structure by lifting individual sections weighing up to 400 tons from barges to a height of 200 feet above water level.

Edward M. Young in this book, *The Great Bridge,* has described these problems of the engineer in a popular, but factually correct, description.

1

The first bridge was a fallen tree. Such a tree, across a ravine or a small stream, naturally provided a dry and safe path across an obstacle. This type of bridge was used by man when he was little more than a beast. His first bridge span was a gift of nature. Later on his growing intelligence indicated that he could place bridges where he wanted them by simply imitating nature, and placing logs across these obstacles.

It is quite likely that man discovered the form of the suspension bridge about the same time that he discovered the simple span. For example, a heavy vine, growing or blown across a ravine, enabled him to get from one side to the other swinging by his hands in a monkey-like fashion. Much later, in quest of a safer and easier crossing he learned to hang two vines or plaited ropes separately so that he could deck them with sticks or a woven netting and in this way crawl across. Ultimately the two vines became four; two below to support a deck, two above to serve as handlines that allowed him to walk across upright.

When man learned that by tieing the upper and lower vines together he gained stability and strength in his bridge, he had learned the fundamentals of suspension bridge construction. Because effective suspension bridges of surprising length have been found in even the most primitive societies of South America, Africa and Australia, it is apparent that the ability of the suspension bridge to span great distances was recognized by even the most undeveloped societies. Paradoxically, however, as man advanced he abandoned the suspension bridge in favor of other types of structures, notably the arch. For while vine and rope bridges were suitable for foot travel they could not carry heavy or concentrated loads.

This problem was solved by the stone arch, which reached its peak of use in the time of the Romans. To move their armies and maintain their empire, they needed roads and the roads needed bridges. Because the stone arch bridge was known to be stable, because it could be built with materials that are in most places readily available and because its prime requisite was tremendous manpower—a commodity that was plentiful and inexpensive in the days of the slave and the peasant, the arch bridge maintained its predominance from the days of the Romans until the early part of the nineteenth century.

Then the very factors that so long favored stone arch construction began to work against it. The use of vast numbers of nameless men became uneconomical. With the development of wrought iron, cast iron and later steel, it became possible to build longer structures in less time with far fewer men and far less materials. This was particularly important in river crossings because as the size of river craft increased, the closeness of stone arch piers interfered with all but the smallest of boats and barges.

The stone arch has never lost its importance and probably never will, but except in U.S. National Parks, where the desire

May 16, 1960.
Brooklyn tower pier site. Driving the cylindrical sheeting
for the construction of the cofferdam.

2

to maintain natural beauty exceeds the need for speed and economy, few stone arches of any size are built today. Arch bridges are not uncommon on highway overpasses but for the most part they are relatively small, and they are made of concrete.

Larger arch bridges are usually made of lightweight, high strength steels. A good example is the Bayonne Bridge between Staten Island and New Jersey; it is the largest arch in the world, with a span of 1,652 feet. Under current engineering practice arches are generally not economical for spans longer than 2,000 feet, and most are less than 1,000. At the same time the suspension bridge is usually not economical for spans of less than 1,000 feet.

In the last century (and even as late as 1930) when engineers were still learning the special characteristics of suspension bridges, some relatively short spans (700 to 1,000 feet) were erected. John Roebling, father of the cable suspension bridge, constructed an 821 foot single span railroad bridge near Niagara Falls, which was completed in 1855. The most famous suspension bridge of all, Brooklyn Bridge, started in 1869 by John Roebling and finished 14 years later by his son Washington, has a mainspan of only 1,595 feet but even this with its two 930 foot sidespans has a total suspended length of 3,455 feet.

The comparative length of sidespans and mainspans in relation to the overall length of a suspension bridge, is a subject of controversy among construction buffs. When an issue of *Engineering News-Record* carried at the same time a story crediting the Verrazano-Narrows Bridge with having the world's longest span, and an advertisement saying that the Mackinac Straits Bridge is the longest suspension bridge in the world, the editors received many letters asking for an explanation. Actually, both the story, and the advertisement, were correct in their claims.

A study of the table of long span bridges found at the back of this book, shows that the Straits bridge has a total suspended length of 7,400 feet while the Narrows bridge has a total suspended length of 6,690 feet. On the basis of these figures the length of the Straits bridge exceeds that of the Narrows Bridge by 710 feet.

The main criteria for the magnitude of a suspension bridge is the length of its mainspan and the load it carries. In this respect the Narrows with 4,260 foot span exceeds the Mackinac by 460 feet, and in weight suspended between towers it is about five times heavier. It carries on two decks twelve lanes of vehicular traffic against the four on the Mackinac. Thus while Mackinac is rightly called the longest suspension bridge, it ranks from the standpoint of magnitude behind the Narrows Bridge as well as the George Washington, the Golden Gate and several other much shorter bridges of its kind.

The main span of the Narrows Bridge is the longest ever built. Its cost—$325 million—makes it one of, if not the most, expensive single structures ever built. Its towers rising 693 feet above the water are higher than most of Manhattan's skyscrapers. On the Brooklyn side its tower foundations go 17 stories below the ground. Its 4 main cables, each 3 feet in diameter and over 7,200 feet long, comprise more than 100,000 pencil thick steel wires whose total length would reach more than five times around the earth at the equator. The massive concrete blocks that anchor the ends of these cables into the ground each contain almost a quarter of a million cubic yards

May 17, 1960.
Staten Island tower pier site. Completed cylindrical
sheeting for the cofferdam.

4

of concrete. To make room for the anchorage on the Staten Island side, the contractor had to dig a hole almost a city block wide and 105 feet deep and had to carry away more than half a million cubic yards of dirt and rock.

So much for the steel and concrete: the bridge is more; it is the fruition of the dreams of men who for generations have imagined spanning the choppy waters of New York harbor to provide a solid link between Staten Island and the other four boroughs of New York. In spite of political affiliations the island has always had closer physical ties to New Jersey than to its own state, mainly because the waters separating it from New Jersey are much narrower and less treacherous than those separating it from New York.

As a result, the islanders have been able to travel to New Jersey by rail since the turn of the century and by automobile since 1928, when the Outerbridge crossing and the Goethals Bridge were completed. In 1931 a third bridge, the Bayonne, was completed.

But until the building of the Narrows Bridge, the island's only connections with New York were ferries that crossed the harbor between the island, Manhattan, and Brooklyn. Under normal conditions the five mile crossing to Manhattan could be made in half an hour, the mile crossing to Brooklyn in about ten minutes. But if the Bay was heavy with ice, or if a fog suddenly closed in, either trip could take much longer. And on clear days when the ferries had no trouble in making their crossings on schedule, they were often so crowded, particularly on summer weekends, that drivers had to wait for hours to get on one. On the bridge the crossing to Brooklyn can be made in three or four minutes.

July 20, 1960.
Concreting the Brooklyn tower base steel cutting edge.

2

From colonial times the width of the Hudson River, and the height of the Palisades on its west bank, formed a barrier to travel between New England and the colonies to the south and west of New York. Therefore a Staten Island crossing involving a ferry from Brooklyn to the north east shore of the island and another from the west side of the island to the low profile of New Jersey offered the safest and speediest route through the New York area and across the harbor. To this end ferries of some sort have been maintained on this route since the early 1700's. By the time of the Revolution Staten Island ferries were running regularly.

In 1810, a 16 year old Staten Island native began both his experience in transportation and the accumulation of one of the country's great fortunes by owning and operating a ferry between the island and New York. That boy, Cornelius Vander-

September 27, 1960.
Staten Island tower pier site. "Operation Dig."

8

bilt, is today perhaps best remembered for the development and consolidation of railroads, but that phase of his life came long after he had earned the title of Commodore by virtue of owning one of the first and largest fleets of steamboats of this time. This commercial empire grew from the small sail ferry across New York Bay and the Narrows.

By 1888, however, demands for a fixed crossing were common. Periodically some politician, citizen, or civic organization would seek action on a bridge across the Narrows. All such proposals were dismissed by the military before they got past the talking stage, on the grounds that destruction of the bridge by an enemy in time of war could conceivably bottle up any part of the Navy in the harbor or in the Brooklyn Navy Yard, thus seriously handicapping our fighting potential.

As an alternative, Federal agencies suggested a tunnel. Early in 1921 the New York State legislature authorized construction of a twin tube railway tunnel under the Narrows on a line almost directly beneath the present bridge. By April of that year contractors were at work on a shaft on the Brooklyn side, and within three months, on the Staten Island side.

The anticipated cost of the tunnel was $30 million, but by the time the shafts were completed it was obvious that the bores would cost more than $60 million. In consequence the work was stopped.

In spite of this experience a tunnel was proposed in 1929 and again in 1937. In both cases funds were allocated for preliminary studies but the earlier try was stopped by the depression, the later one by World War II.

In 1945 the tunnel was again revived, but when in the following year the New York Tunnel Authority was merged with the Triborough Bridge Authority to form the Triborough Bridge and Tunnel Authority (TBTA), the situation was reappraised. The conclusion: a bridge would cost less to build and maintain, could be built faster, and would have a greater traffic capacity.

October 14, 1960.
Staten Island tower base. Placing the
"cooky-cutters"—the dredging well steel forms.

That same year the New York State Legislature authorized construction of the bridge. By this time the development of nuclear weapons made senseless any opposition to the bridge on the grounds that its destruction would bottle up warships in New York harbor. The military, however, was still very much concerned with the bridge. The most sensible place to build the structure was between two projections of land extending into the bay, making the crossing as short as possible. These projections of land were occupied by Fort Wadsworth on Staten Island and Fort Hamilton in Brooklyn.

While neither fort ever fired a shot in anger, and while their value as defense installations had long since disappeared, the Army was not inclined to give up any part of them without suitable compensation. However, after long negotiations, the Bridge Authority got the land it needed for the bridge and its approach roads and the Army replaced its lost land and buildings with some $26 million worth of new installations, paid for by the Authority.

Long before the negotiations with the Army were completed, the Authority had awarded the job of designing the structure to Ammann & Whitney, a New York consulting firm, headed by Othmar H. Ammann, a man with an incredible record for big bridge design.

One of his great achievements, the George Washington Bridge, which spans the Hudson River between New York and New Jersey, was considered to be the eighth wonder of the world when it was opened in 1931. Not only was it the heaviest suspension bridge ever built, but its mainspan was more than twice the length of the second longest. In many respects it is one of the most beautiful and remarkable structures ever built.

As chief engineer of the Port of New York Authority from 1929 to 1939, Mr. Ammann was responsible for the design and construction of the three previously mentioned bridges linking Staten Island with New Jersey.

During this period he was also Chief Engineer of the Bridge Authority for two notable suspension bridges within New York

March 17, 1961.
Brooklyn anchorage site. Timber supports for moving
Dover Patrol Monument to its new location.

City, the Triborough Bridge, which links the Bronx with Manhattan and Queens, and the Bronx-Whitestone which spans the East River and links the Bronx with Queens. As partner of Ammann & Whitney he designed the Throgs Neck Bridge across the East River at its confluence with Long Island Sound. He also played an important role in the design of the Golden Gate Bridge in San Francisco, and many other projects.

Mr. Ammann now in his eighties, busies himself with the designs of even longer spans than that of the Narrows. But regardless of achievements before or after the Narrows Bridge project, the design of this structure is in itself a magnificent accomplishment for one man's lifetime in this field.

May 23, 1961.
Initial preparation for concreting Staten Island anchorage.

3

Within broad limits, a building can be designed in any size and shape that suits the whim of an engineer, architect or owner. A bridge, on the other hand, must be designed to suit many conditions beyond human control. Length of span, required clearances, type and volume of traffic, water depths, subsurface conditions, approach routes—these are but a few of the many factors that must influence—and to some extent, limit —the bridge designer's freedom of choice.

Yet a bridge, particularly a large bridge, is not merely a structure. It is also a link in a transportation system, and as such it will be viewed by countless thousands (or, as in the case of the Narrows Bridge, millions) of people on the move every year. Therefore, a designer must tax his ability to produce a structure that is not only functional, but also attractive. Almost any picture of the Narrows Bridge bespeaks the success of the

May 25, 1961.
Staten Island tower base.
Concreting of granite encased pedestals.

designer in creating a beautiful structure, in spite of the limitations inherent in bridge design.

In granting permission for the construction of the Narrows Bridge, the Department of the Army, and specifically the Corps of Engineers, which has responsibility for all navigable waters in the United States, required that the bridge deck must clear the center of the 2,000 foot wide channel by at least 216 feet. The Corps also required that the deck at the towers be at least 180 feet above the water.

By using a 4% grade—that is by raising the roadway 4 feet in every 100 feet of length—on the approach ramps and the side spans, and by gracefully curving the main deck, a minimum clearance of 228 feet was obtained at midspan.

The location of the towers and the position of the anchorages —both factors in establishing span lengths—were determined partly by navigation requirements and partly by physical conditions at the site. These in turn, by using an economical and graceful curve of the main cables, established the criteria for the height of the towers, and ultimately the amount of steel, concrete and wire needed for the bridge.

When the government originally granted permission for construction of the bridge over the Narrows, its planned position was north of its present location and both its ends were on private property. In this location the bridge would have had a main span of 4,620 feet. After the Army later agreed to permit construction of the bridge on its present location, with its ends on land within the army forts, it was possible for the engineers to reduce the mainspan length by 360 feet. This effected savings in materials and construction time, and consequently in costs, for the longer the central span, the heavier it must be throughout.

Construction of a suspension bridge involves a multitude of considerations. The consultant's drawings of the bridge numbered more than 1,500. The drawings made by contractors of the countless components ran into the tens of thousands. At one time an engineer for Bethlehem Steel Company, which

July 18, 1961.
Staten Island tower piers. Removal of cellular cofferdam.

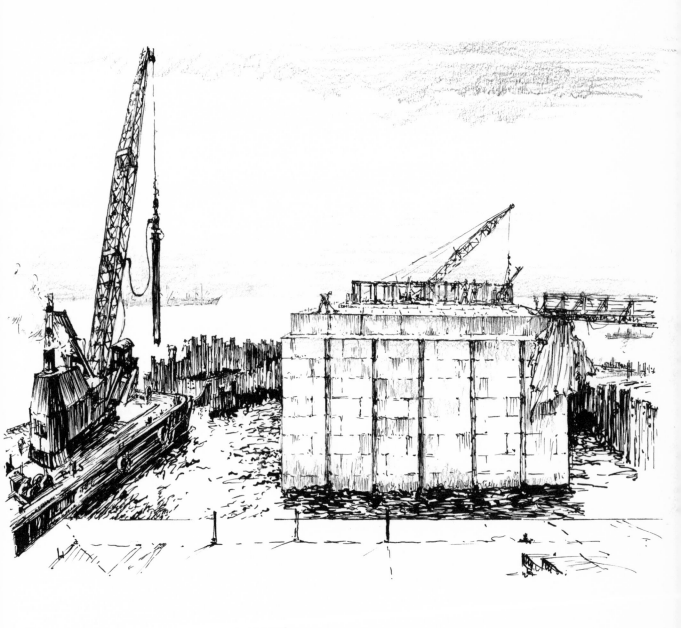

built the Staten Island tower, only half jokingly reported that the detailing was nearly finished because the plans on hand then weighed almost as much as the tower would when it was erected. The 26,000 tons of plates and angles that make up one tower are held together by about 1½ million field-installed bolts and about twice that number of shop-installed rivets. Since each of these bolts goes through two, three, and sometimes four or more pieces of steel, the planners had to plot the position of more than ten million holes, each of which had to line up exactly with one or more other holes. Thus, just figuring where to put air space in the form of a hole, was a major operation.

July 21, 1961.
Staten Island tower piers. Grinding and
polishing of pedestals.

4

Complex as a suspension bridge is, it can be considered to consist of just five major components: the deck, which carries the traffic; the cables which support the deck; the towers which support the cables; the tower foundations which support the towers, and the anchorages which hold the ends of the cables in place.

Because the tops of the two massive tower foundations are several feet below water, they are not a visible part of the bridge. Except for the engineers who had to keep check on them, it is improbable that even the men who worked on the superstructure ever gave them much thought. It is almost certain that the average traveler using the bridge or the sightseer viewing it will not think of them as part of the bridge.

Yet these foundations are most important components of the bridge. They support the entire weight of both the suspended

March 30, 1962.
During construction of the Brooklyn anchorage.

structure and the towers—a total of 264,000 tons. They also
support the total weight of all the vehicles that might be on
the bridge at any one time. (For design purposes the weight
of the vehicles, called the "live load," was estimated at 16,000
tons although actually it will probably never come anywhere
near that figure.)

To support these tremendous loads, the tower foundations
have to be big, they have to be strong, and they have to be well
founded.

Each of the piers is a rectangular, open-dredged, cellular
concrete caisson, a structure designed primarily to carry foundation materials to firm ground. In the case of the Narrows
Bridge it was a vertically perforated, steel encased concrete
block built in sections above water and sunk by a combination

of its own weight and the removal of the earth beneath it. If either caisson could be seen from above, even now, it would look like a gigantic pegboard, 229 feet long, 129 feet wide and riddled with regularly spaced holes each 17 feet in diameter.

Seen from the side, each would look like a windowless steel skyscraper. And while the caissons go down instead of up, their comparison with a skyscraper is reasonable, for on the Staten Island side, the caisson extends more than 10 stories below the water; on the Brooklyn side, more than 17 stories. Thus, in spite of the holes, the Staten Island pier contains more than 79,000 cubic yards of concrete and 9.4 million pounds of reinforcing steel while the Brooklyn pier contains 117,000 cubic yards of concrete and almost 13 million pounds of reinforcing steel.

Preparation for the piers began long before any construction contractors appeared on the scene. As early as 1954 specialists were busy making borings—that is drilling 4 inch diameter, pipe-encased holes as deep as 354 feet to determine soil bearing capacity and to get soil samples at various depths, or "elevations," to use the language of the engineers. In all, the drillers made 31 such borings.

Ideally the foundations would rest directly on, or in, rock. But at Staten Island the boring contractors had to drill almost 200 feet before they encountered even a decomposed rock and at the site of the Brooklyn pier they had to go more than 300 feet to reach good rock. Carrying foundations to these depths is not impossible, but it would have been very difficult and expensive.

Fortunately, far above the rock on both sides there are layers of earth firm enough to support the weight of the bridge. On the Staten Island side, where geologists believe the earth was compressed during the last glacial period by a sheet of ice at least 270 feet thick, there is a tough stratum 105 feet below water. In Brooklyn where the earth is not as compact, the designers decided to carry the pier to a depth of 170 feet below water.

1962.
Brooklyn tower. Erection of creeper derrick.

24

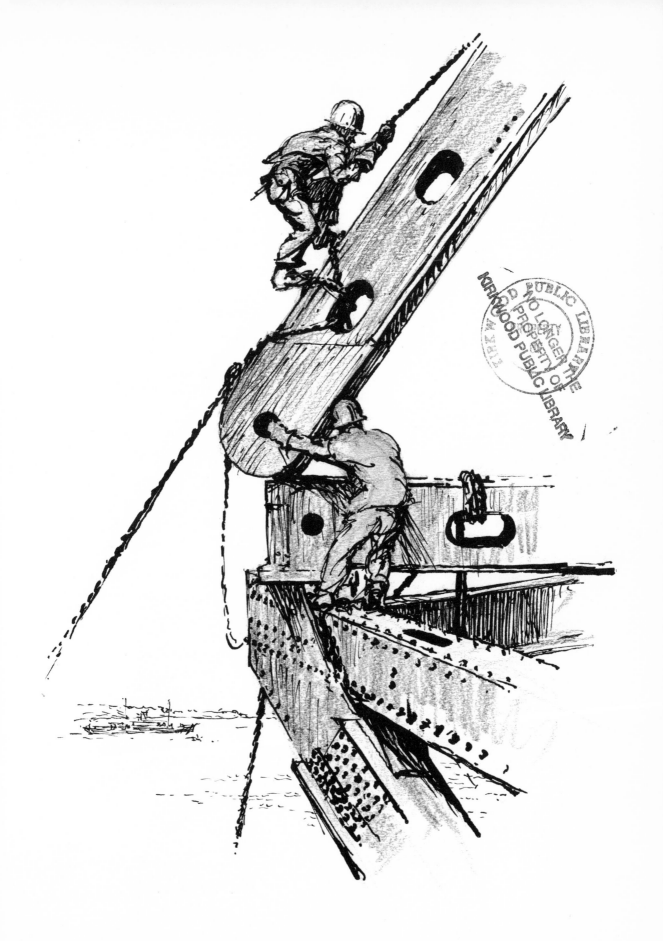

117008

The Staten Island tower is located in shallow water about 200 feet off shore. The Brooklyn tower is on the site of a small man-made island that for many years was a Navy installation known as Fort Lafayette.

To determine the exact location of the tower piers the engineers used conventional surveying methods. The tapes used for measuring were calibrated by the United States Bureau of Standards under specific tensions, and at a predetermined temperature. When surveyors used these tapes they pulled them with a measured tension. They also noted the air temperature at the time of each measurement, and corrected their readings to compensate for any expansion or contraction of the tapes resulting from temperature changes.

Because of these procedures and constant cross-checking the engineers were able to make measurements and establish base lines having a possible error of less than 1 in 200,000.

The piers were spotted by triangulation. Ten surveyors, five on each side of the bay, made four complete sets of observations. Then the survey parties switched sides and repeated their observations from the opposite shore. As a final precaution against error, in measurements across the water the engineers used a Tellurometer, an instrument that makes use of reflected radio beams to measure distances.

Taking cognizance of the difficulties of building these two huge structures under as much as 175 feet of mud and tidewater, the TBTA allowed a total of 610 days for construction of the Staten Island tower pier and 790 calendar days for the Brooklyn tower pier. To make sure that the job would be completed on time the authority subjected the contractor to a charge of $10,000 a day for every calendar day that he ran behind schedule on completion on either of the piers. Both piers were completed in less than the allowed time; the Staten Island pier was finished in just under a year and a half, the Brooklyn pier in just over two years.

April 3, 1962.
Anchorage construction, Staten Island.
Start of erection of eye-bar chains.

Although the caissons that make up the tower piers were designed to be sunk through mud and water, they had to be started on sand. It was therefore necessary for the contractor to erect a structure that would exclude water from the pier site. It was also to his advantage to have this same structure provide storage space for materials and working area for his machines.

Under some conditions it is possible for a contractor to build sand islands that will serve both these purposes, but at the Narrows, such islands were not feasible. The tides and currents are too swift, the water too deep, the bottom too unstable, and the sites too close to the channel.

For these reasons the contractor installed cofferdams around both pier sites. On the Staten Island side the cofferdam was made up of interlocking steel sheet piling driven vertically into the ground as a series of 49 foot diameter cylinders each connected to those adjacent by curved partitions or "diaphragms," also of steel sheet piling. There were 16 of these cylinders and each was firmly embedded in the ground under the water. The tops of the sheets were driven to, or cut off at, an elevation about 10 feet above high water. The resulting cells were then filled to the top with sand so they were stable, and so that the contractor would have a level area completely around the pier location on which he could store materials and run the cranes, loaders and other equipment needed for installation of the tower pier. On the Brooklyn side, where part of the pier was set on the island, the contractor did not need as many cells, installing just 10.

The initial work on the cofferdams was all done from floating derrick boats, but as the cells were completed, the contractor was able to put land machines on top to help out with construction.

At each side, before the cofferdam was closed, the contractor floated into it barges loaded with sand that was dumped to provide a firm but workable bottom inside. When the coffer-

April 4, 1962.
Staten Island tower construction.

28

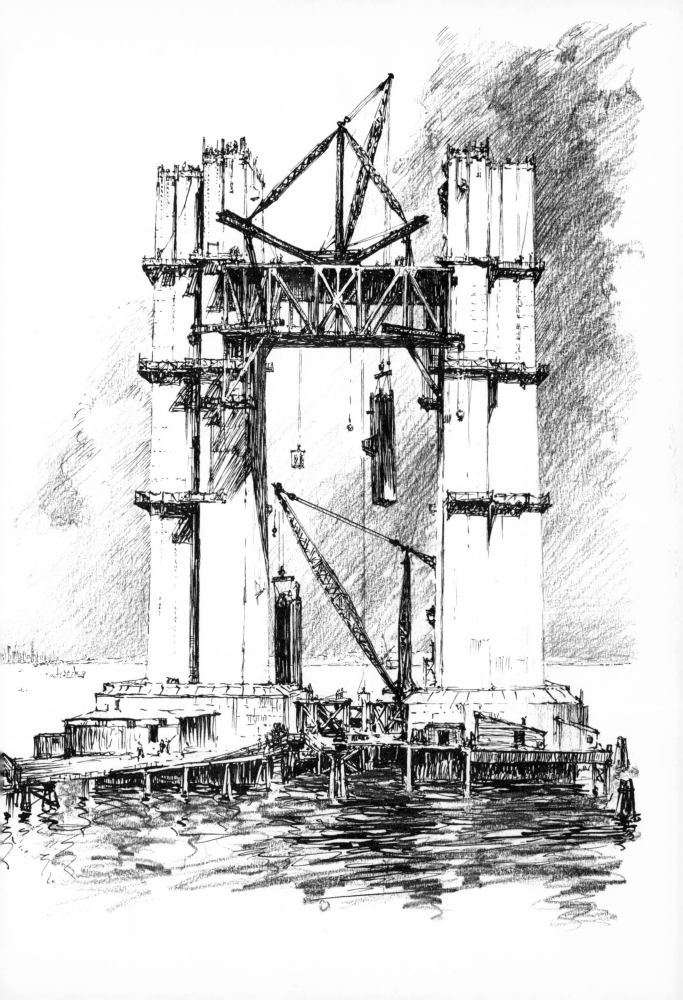

dams were completed, the contractor pumped out the water then leveled the sand inside as a base for the caisson.

The bottom edge of both caissons, and the part first set, is a steel "cutting edge." This was delivered to the job in trough-like sections, 37 to 49 feet long, 7 feet high, about a foot wide at the closed bottom and 5 feet wide at the open top. These sections were accurately placed on the sand with the narrow edge down, and were welded together to form the rectangular perimeter of the caisson. At third points on each side of the box made by the outside cutting edge, the interior cutting edges were set and welded. The complete cutting edge formed one big rectangle divided into 9 rectangular compartments.

In appearance and in use, a cutting edge of this type resembles a gigantic multiple cookie-cutter, and logically enough caissons started with this device are commonly called "cookie-cutter caissons."

Within the troughs formed by the sideplates of the cutting edges, iron-workers set both horizontal and vertical reinforcing steel, and masons then filled the edges with concrete. The concrete makes the edge solid and gives it weight. The steel within the concrete provides rigidity; that extending above it provides for a bond with the caisson sections to come.

The contractor next filled all the compartments within the perimeter of the cutting edge with sand that was brought to the site by barges and placed with clamshell buckets. This sand served two purposes; it stabilized the cutting edge and it served as a bottom form for the next part of the caisson, a 6 foot high transition section consisting of concrete walls intersecting like the lines on a checkerboard to form 66 chambers each 17 feet square. These chambers, called square dredging wells, were also filled with sand. The contractor was then ready to begin with construction of the major portion of the caisson, the part containing cylindrical digging wells.

The procedures used in this phase of construction are highly repetitive, but they required careful planning and extreme

May 18, 1962.
Staten Island tower erection, 10th tier,
and Brooklyn tower, 2nd tier.

care and control. Basically, they involved adding concrete to the caisson to make it heavier and higher, while digging dirt out from beneath it, so that it could sink.

Over each of the square digging wells, the contractor set a steel cylinder, 17 feet in diameter, 10 feet high, and open at both ends. On top but 4 inches inside the perimeter of the concrete block that makes up the square digging wells, the contractor stood 10 foot high steel forms. These contain the outside wall of concrete to come. At this point the caisson resembled a huge steel box containing within it 66 enormous cans. As the side forms and the interior cans were set, ironworkers were busy lacing all the open spaces, except those within the cans, with reinforcing steel.

Meanwhile, carpenters set up bulkheads within the form to divide it into smaller sections. There are two main reasons for these bulkheads. First, filling the entire caisson form to its 10 foot height would require more than 5,000 cubic yards of concrete—far more than the contractor could pour in a single day. To get the job into manageable size, he had to break it up into smaller units; this he did with the bulkheads. A second and perhaps more important reason is that the caisson sinks largely under its own weight, and it is steered on its downward trip by the proper positioning of this weight. It is not enough to maintain an even distribution of weight completely across the caisson because the ground underneath does not always offer a uniform resistance. Thus, just as it is often impossible to put a lid on a shoe polish can by simply pushing it in the middle, so the contractor often had to put a little more pressure on one part of the caisson than on another in order to keep it moving down in a vertical plane.

While concrete was being added to the top of the caisson, cranes carrying clam-shell buckets were busy removing dirt from under the caisson so that it could move downward. The buckets were lowered through the cylindrical digging wells so that they could grab dirt from the big rectangular openings formed within the steel cutting edges at the bottom.

July 5, 1962.
Erecting roadway supporting steel.

32

All the while that the caissons were being built up, dug out and sunk, engineers were busy measuring the settlement. If it appeared that one side or another was "hung up" on stubborn dirt below, the clamshells worked harder and longer in that area. When a particularly hard mass of earth or rock remained packed under the perimeter of the cutting edge during the sinking, the contractor dislodged it with high pressure water jets.

After the caisson was seated, its under side was cleaned with jets, some of which were built right into the caisson. Others which were lowered through the digging wells were made to revolve while sending great streams of water outward and upward beneath the concrete part of the caisson but within the steel cutting edges. In action, they worked much the same as a garden hose aimed directly at a lawn at close range, but on an infinitely greater scale, since they discharged water at pressures of up to 300 pounds per square inch.

As each 10 foot lift of concrete was completed, the contractor raised his forms and set them up for the succeeding lift. The straight forms that shaped the outside of the caisson were lifted up in sections by cranes; the cylindrical forms that shaped the digging wells were merely squeezed together so they became smaller in diameter; they were then lifted, opened to their proper size, and reset by cranes.

At the start of the caisson work, where the earth was fairly soft, the speed at which the caisson settled was determined largely by the speed at which the contractor could place concrete. Later, when the bottom of the caisson was in hard earth far below the surface, the downward speed was dependent more on how fast the cranes could dig. For the most part the settlement of the caissons was so gradual that it was not noticeable. Occasionally, however, it was not only noticeable but actually frightening. Once when the bottom of the Brooklyn caisson was about 159 feet below water, the entire mass dropped 4 feet 3 inches in only three seconds. Later when the bottom was 163 feet below water, the caison dropped 6 feet 2 inches

July 13, 1962.
Brooklyn tower. Erection of 5th tier.

34

in five seconds. In both cases the earth beneath the caisson had been removed but the caisson was prevented from settling by friction resulting from the pressure of the earth on the sides. The settlements came only after the contractor reduced this friction by injecting air and water into the ground around the perimeter of the caisson through jets built into the structure for that purpose.

When the caissons were sunk to the proper elevations, the chambers within the cutting edges were cleaned with water jets that churned up the dirt and stones within the chamber and put it into suspension so that it could be removed with air lifts.

An air lift works much the same as a fish tank filter except that where the filter traps the dirt, the airlift brings it up. Air is sent down a small pipe or hose under high pressure and injected near the base of a larger pipe which is open at the bottom end. As the air enters the larger pipe it aerates the water in it. The aerated water is much less dense than the water outside the pipe and therefore it rises rapidly enough to create a suction at the open end. The suction draws in not only nearby water but also any suspended material in the water. All this is carried to the top of the caisson and discharged over the side. So effective were the air lifts that stones as big as 2 inches in diameter were sometimes removed from the caissons.

At this stage of construction, the caissons were supported to some extent by the friction of the earth pressing against their sides. Mainly, however, they were supported by the hard earth directly under the cutting edges at the bottom, but only at the cutting edges, since all the area within them was cleaned of earth and contained only water. To increase the bearing capacity of the caissons, the contractor had to fill this space with concrete.

Now, if concrete is simply dumped loose into water, its ingredients will separate. The stone, being heaviest, will fall fastest. The sand will follow. Cement, being finely ground and having light particles, will remain in suspension in the water

September 9, 1962.
Brooklyn tower. Preparation of tower sections for erection.

for some time and if there is any current, will drift off with it. For this reason the contractor poured the concrete into the water-filled cells through a "tremie," a funnel-topped 12 inch diameter pipe long enough to reach from the bottom of the caisson to the top. This pipe was held by one crane so that its bottom was just off the bottom of the excavation under the caisson. The concrete was handled by another crane.

Before each pour a burlap plug was pushed into the pipe in order to keep the water in the tremie from diluting the concrete. When the poured concrete reached the bottom of pipe it forced out the plug and spread out, displacing water. As the concrete raised in the chambers, the tremie was raised so that the concrete could continue to flow, but never lifted so high that the bottom end was free of the previously poured mix.

The tremie concreting of both caissons continued until the nine large chambers within the cutting edges were filled, and until the 66 square transition wells were partly filled. The circular digging wells were not filled, and in fact were not even pumped dry. They remain today filled with water, and they will remain so for as long as the bridge stands.

Across the top of the caisson the contractor then cast a 4 foot thick slab of reinforced concrete designed to distribute across the caisson the weight of the superstructure. On this distribution slab the contractor next built the two pedestals that support the legs of each tower. These pedestals are 63 feet wide, and 76 feet long. They extend from the top of the slab, 4 feet below water to a point about 32 feet above water. The main purpose of this height is to protect the steel tower legs from the salt water of the bay. For aesthetic reasons and for further protection, the outside surfaces of the pedestals are surfaced with granite.

Within each pedestal there are 54 bolts that hold the base of the towers in place. These bolts are 3 inches in diameter, almost 22 feet long and are embedded 16 feet into concrete.

Because of the ratio of the tower height to the tower base length and width a difference of even ½ inch in the levelness

Spring 1962.
Staten Island anchorage. Erection of eye-bar framing for cables.

38

of the pedestal top could throw the towers more than 6 inches out of plumb. Therefore, before the base plates of the towers could be set on the pedestals it was necessary that the contact surfaces be absolutely level and smooth. The contractor set up rails on the top of the pedestals and on them mounted cutting and grinding machines that moved back and forth to level the concrete that the base plate would rest on.

While the pedestals were being completed, the contractor was busy removing the cofferdams from around their perimeters. On the Brooklyn side, he also dredged away the remnants of the island on which part of the pier was built.

When all this work was finished, the waters of the bay closed forever over the $16 million worth of steel and concrete that support the bridge, completely hiding the physical results of more than 2½ years of around-the-clock work by hundreds of men, and leaving only four relatively small columns of stone-covered concrete as evidence that there is anything at all below the water.

1962.
Brooklyn tower. Preparing to "hook on" tower sections.

5

Basically the two anchorages located at each end of the Narrows Bridge are just what their name indicates—anchors for the ends of the four cables that support the suspended structure. They consist of huge blocks of concrete that accomplish their purpose by a combination of their own weight and their friction against the earth in which they are set.

But each is more than just an anchor. At its inshore end each supports the bridge approaches. At its outshore end each carries four massive, roller-mounted saddles that support, and move with, the cables as they change length, either because of temperature changes or changes in the weight they carry. These saddles also permit the round cables to be splayed outward into strands so that their pull is distributed over a wide area and through a great mass of concrete.

March 18, 1963.
Brooklyn anchorage. Start of "spinning" of main cables.

The wires of the cables are connected to the concrete by means of huge eye-bars—great pieces of steel plate cut in the shape of a characteristic dog bone with a hole in each of the enlarged ends.

There are 1,952 of these eye-bars, each from 22 to 54 feet long. They vary in thickness, and some weigh as much as 5 tons each. They are set up in groups of three links to form eye-bar chains. Each chain has at its bottom end a single heavy eye-bar that is tied into the concrete by a pin. At the top end another pin links this bottom bar to two others, one on each side. The top of these two bars straddle another single bar to

form a system that resembles a tremendously magnified and elongated bicycle chain. In the completed anchorage, the upper two links of the chains are free to move up and down so as to maintain a straight pull between the anchorage and the cable strands, which are looped over the upper end of the top eye-bar.

Everything about the anchorages is intricately tied in not only with the design factors of the rest of the bridge, but also with the topographic and geologic conditions of the soil in which they are placed.

The position of both anchorages for the Narrows Bridge was determined largely by the conditions existing on the Brooklyn shore. A multi-lane highway running adjacent to the shore line made it impractical to set that anchorage too close to the water. At the same time a hill inshore of the highway provided a good place for the anchorage since it would cover and conceal some of the mass concrete needed and at the same time provide elevated ground for the approach roads from the Brooklyn side of the structure. On the Staten Island side an even higher hill offered the same advantages and made it possible for the engineers to balance the sidespans (the spans between the towers and the anchorages) at 1,215 feet each by placing the Brooklyn anchorage about 500 feet inside the shore line and the Staten Island anchorage about 900 feet inland.

To the casual viewer each of the anchorages looks like a single wedge-shaped block of concrete, extending high above the ground at the river side and sloping off to nothing at the inshore side. Actually each consists of many blocks of concrete poured separately but joined together by keys and reinforcing steel and each extends far below the ground. The visable part of the anchorages—the upper 130 feet—look, and are, about the same. Each is the size of a football field—160 feet wide, 300 feet long. Below ground however, there is a difference and as a result the Brooklyn anchorage contains some 207,000 cubic yards of concrete while the one on Staten Island contains only 171,000 cubic yards. The reason for this is that the soil on the

March 21, 1963.
Storm-guy system for catwalk.
Brooklyn tower in foreground.

44

Brooklyn side is not as firm as that on Staten Island, so the foundations in Brooklyn had to be set deeper and made bigger.

The placement of the anchorage foundations, like everything else on the bridge was determined only after intensive study. In 1954 when boring contractors were taking samples of the soil for the tower foundations, they were also working at the anchorage sites, and here too they drilled as deep as 350 feet. Ideally, the anchorages, like the towers, would be founded on rock, but at the anchorages, as at the towers, rock is too far below the surface to make this practical. Therefore, the engineers decided to found the anchorages on compact sand far above the rock. As now installed, the bottom of the anchorage foundation in Brooklyn ranges from 30 feet below the water level of the bay to 9 feet below, while on the Island it ranges from 4 feet below the water level to 16 feet above it.

The reason for the range in the elevation is that the foundation bottoms are not level, but are higher towards the bay. Thus the cables, in trying to pull the anchorages inward would not only have to slide them across the ground but also would have to pull them uphill. The effect of this is well understood by anyone who has ever pulled a sled or pushed a car both on level ground and up a slope.

The resistance offered by the incline beneath the anchorage foundations, coupled with the friction between the foundations and the ground is so great that on the Staten Island anchorage it is equal to that offered by 80,000 tons of concrete. In Brooklyn, where in spite of its greater overall height the anchorage is not so deeply embedded in the earth, these forces provide a stability equal to that of 25,000 tons of concrete. So in both cases, the engineers were able to lighten the anchorages by these respective amounts.

The Staten Island Anchorage was constructed in four stages; the larger Brooklyn anchorage in five. There are several reasons for this. To begin with, while the cable strands cannot be linked to the eye-bars until the bottoms of the eye-bars are fixed in the anchorage, neither can the eye-bars be completely

March 1963.
Brooklyn anchorage. Placing loop of wire over spinning wheel.

encased in concrete until after all the strands are attached to them. This means that the contractor had to cast enough concrete to anchor the eye-bars, then wait until after the cable spinning contractor had attached the cable strands to them before completing the concreting.

Because the anchorages rest on sand rather than rock, they are bound to settle slightly under their own weight. To minimize this settlement, the engineers computed the uplift that the cables would effect on the anchorage as the deck sections were attached, and they coordinated much of the concrete placement with deck erection. Thus, as more and more steel was erected, and the cable strands exerted a greater pull on the anchorages, concrete was added to counteract the pull without appreciably increasing the pressures exerted on the ground by the foundations.

A factor which limited the amount of concrete that could be cast at one time even within each stage of anchorage construction is the heat of "hydration." When the solid ingredients of concrete—sand, stone and cement—are mixed with water, they form a workable plastic material that will apparently set after a period of time ranging from a few minutes to several hours, depending on numerous circumstances.

Freshly set concrete is by no means a finished product, however. A chemical reaction between the cement and the water (hydration) continues for days or even months, and this reaction generates heat. So great is the heat of hydration that, if uncontrolled, it can cause the water to boil and become steam. This steam, locked in the concrete creates pressures that form voids making the concrete pourous and therefore weak.

On jobs that require continuous casting of thousands of cubic yards of concrete—large dams, for instance—it is not uncommon to cast the concrete around refrigeration pipes that can cool the material for months after it has been placed.

On the Narrows anchorages, the heat of hydration was kept below 132 degrees Fahrenheit. Individual pours were limited to 1,500 cubic yards and—except in winter—shaved ice replaced

March 25, 1963.
Brooklyn approach. Concreting on upper deck.

48

part of the water used in mixing concrete. For example, with an air temperature of 75 degrees F., each cubic yard of concrete would be made with 16 gallons of water and 125 pounds of ice which, when melted, would become about 15 gallons of water. In this way the concrete was usually placed at an initial temperature of less than 60 degrees F.

While the two anchorages were similar in design, their site conditions differed greatly. So too did the contractor's methods of construction.

The contractor's first problem in Brooklyn was an 80 foot high, 1,000 ton obelisk commemorating the Dover Patrol of World War I. This monument had to be moved from the site of the anchorage to a site 503 feet away; it had to be turned 90 degrees so that its inscription would face a street. The contractor could have dismantled the obelisk and reassembled it on its new location, but he chose to move it in one piece. To do this he dug trenches beneath it, and through these he slid steel beams to support the foundation. He then used hydraulic jacks to raise the monument 7 feet in the air so that he could place a steel beam track beneath it. By placing steel rollers between the track beams and the supporting beams, he was able to winch the heavy but slender needle to its new location.

With the monument out of the way the contractor then began tackling the major problems of the Brooklyn anchorage construction—ground water and lack of space. The hole for the anchorage had to be dug through porous ground to a distance some 30 feet below the nearby bay.

Anyone who has tried to dig a hole in sand at a beach can understand the contractor's problems. When the bottom of the hole reaches the level of the water nearby, the water enters it through the sides and the bottom making further digging impossible. Removing water from inside the hole does not help— as fast as it comes out, it is replaced by more water which carries in with it enough sand to keep the bottom of the hole at about the same elevation, no matter how much material is removed. The solution therefore lies in preventing the water from reaching the hole.

1963.
Staten Island tower and main span, showing
the cable-squeezing apparatus.

50

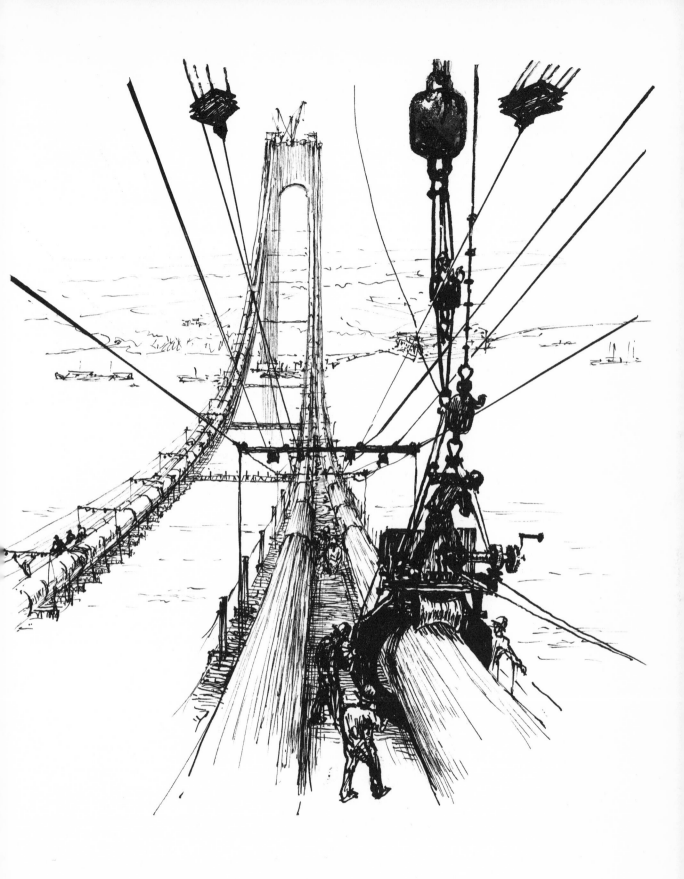

For the anchorages, this was done by ringing the outside of the excavation with a wellpoint system. Wellpoints are basically small diameter pipes (1½ to 2 inches) that are installed vertically at close intervals to remove water from the ground before it can run into the hole. The bottom of each pipe is screened to keep solids out, and the top is connected to a large horizontal pipe (12 inches in diameter, in this case) called a header. The header is connected to one or more big pumps that suck the water from the ground for discharge outside the area. Because the excavation was so close to the water and because the ground was so porous, the contractor had to pump for 11 months using three diesel-powered pumps each capable of handling 4,000 gallons of water per minute.

Lack of space played an important role in determining the equipment that the contractor could use for excavating. He used power shovels (still respectfully but erroneously called "steam shovels" by many people, although they haven't been powered by steam since the early 1930's) and cranes carrying clamshell and dragline buckets. The clamshell, which resembles its namesake, is good for digging deep holes and getting into tight corners. The dragline, a four-sided bucket open at the top and one end, gives a smooth floor to an excavation since it is cast ahead of the machine then pulled back towards it, more or less scraping the ground as it digs in.

Storing the excavated dirt was also a problem for the contractor. There was no room at the site so he had to truck all of it away. However, because the hole had to be bigger than the concrete going back into it, more than 80,000 cubic yards of dirt had to be brought back for fill after the anchorage was completed.

The Staten Island anchorage was a different story. Here the contractor had no water problem (because the bottom was higher) and he had plenty of room. To dig this hole he used scrapers—big tractor-drawn bowls with bottoms that drop to scoop up the earth as they move forward. As the bowl is filled, the operator raises the bottom hydraulically and drives to a

July 18, 1963.
Cable eye-bar anchorage, Brooklyn end.

dumping area where he lowers the bottom a little and pushes the dirt out through the opening with hydraulic rams. Some of the scrapers used were able to load and carry away as much as 40 cubic yards of dirt at one time. Thus while the hole for this anchorage was much bigger than that of the one in Brooklyn, it was not as hard to dig.

To make the concrete for the anchorages the contractor set up a concrete plant right at each site. As each batch of concrete was mixed, it was emptied into open-top trucks that carried it where it was needed. At first the trucks were able to dump the concrete directly on the ground or into inclined chutes or narrow tubes called elephant trunks that permitted it to flow where needed. As the concrete got higher the trucks spilled their loads into buckets that were lifted by cranes.

July 19, 1963.
Brooklyn side span and tower during spinning operation.

6

Cut into pieces some 26,000 tons of steel plates and angles. Use more than 3 million rivets to form the pieces into about 400 steel boxes weighing from 35 to 70 tons, and containing between them more than 10,000 steel cells each the size of a telephone booth, but 6 to 16 feet high. Move the boxes many miles by truck and rail and barge. Stand them up one at a time, each in its proper place, side by side, one on top of the other until they form two towering obelisks, smaller at the bottom than an ordinary house but as high as a 70-story skyscraper, and in the process keep them within a quarter of an inch of vertical. Within each obelisk connect up 16 miles of vertical ladders and build two elevators. Join the obelisks 15 stories in the air by a horizontal strut containing 2½ miles of passageways; join them at the top with a 120 foot high arch. Then raise and set above this arch two pairs of steel castings weighing 712 tons. This was the job of the contractors who built the towers.

August 25, 1963.
Brooklyn side span. Erecting first
floor truss, Brooklyn anchorage.

The towers rise 693 feet above the water. Their purpose is to support the bridge cables, and in doing so, to transfer the weight of the suspended structure through their foundations to the earth below.

Each tower is made up of three major integral components: two vertical legs, a horizontal lower strut, and an arched portal strut.

The legs, which are "T" shaped, measure just under 660 feet from top to bottom. They were erected in 16 tiers, which may be likened to stories in a building—but where a building story is generally about 10 feet high, the tiers of the towers, with one exception, were 40 to 48 feet high. The exception, the base tier, is only 24 feet high. The lower strut, which connects the legs at the fourth tier about 150 feet above the water is 28 feet wide, 40 feet high. In addition to stabilizing the legs, this strut supports the roadway as it passes through the tower.

The portal arch, 28 feet wide and 87 feet deep at the center, connects the legs at the 14th, 15th and 16th tiers. It is the principal stabilizing influence at the top of the towers.

From the outside, the towers and the struts look like relatively simple steel tubes and boxes. From the inside, the picture is entirely different. Both the tower legs and the struts are a honeycomb of rectangular steel cells. There are about 10,000 cells in each tower. Most are 3½ feet square, and they range in height from 6½ feet to 16 feet. Each cell can be reached from another through a small manhole in the top, bottom or side.

Within each tower there are 180 separate systems of vertical ladders. Of these systems, 112 run from the bottom of the tower legs to the top; the remaining 68 are shortened by the sloping sides of the legs. On these ladders a man can climb vertically a total of 16 miles without touching the same ladder twice, and without going through any cell twice.

The maze formed by these cells is so complex that men working within them were provided with miners' lamps for their hard hats and maps correlating the location of each cell with numbers painted on the cell walls. In spite of this, men some-

August 30, 1963.
Assembling floor span trusses for main roadway.

58

times became lost and could not find their way out alone. For this reason both contractors established an accurate check-out system, and elevator operators never left the job at night until every man was accounted for.

As intricate as the finished towers may be, the job of detailing and assembling them was far more complex. Both contractors worked against tight schedules; the Staten Island tower contractor had 420 days to complete its work, the Brooklyn tower contractor had only 305. The difference resulted from the longer time that it took to install the larger Brooklyn tower foundation. The cut-off day was about the same for both tower contractors but the starting day in Staten Island preceded that in Brooklyn by more than five months.

To expedite erection both contractors shop-fabricated the tower legs and struts in box-like sections that could be connected on the job. Most of the sections contained four to six cells and weighed between 30 and 70 tons. However, two sections in the Brooklyn pier contained 8 cells and weighed 97 tons, while two sections on the Staten Island tower weighed 94 tons.

The contractor on the Staten Island tower, concerned more with weight than time, fabricated tiers in 16 sections; the Brooklyn contractor compensated for a shorter construction schedule by setting a tier up in 14 sections.

Before either contractor could begin any assembling of parts, he was faced with making drawings of every plate and angle, of figuring the position of every hole. These drawings ran into the thousands, the computations into the tens and hundreds of thousands. Scheduling and logistics were major problems. Every part had to be ready and in the right place at the right time. Units had to be assembled and shipped in the proper sequence. And before any unit could be shipped, it had to be fitted against its adjacent units so that if there were any errors they would be discovered on the ground in the plant, rather than in the air at the job site. The lower struts and the arch struts were completely assembled, and then disassembled in the fabricating shops before they were sent to the job.

Summer 1963.
Cable band being lowered into position.
Brooklyn Belt Parkway below.

Both contractors began their field work by erecting work platforms completely around the tower foundation and by linking these to the shore by sturdy trestles.

The work platforms were rugged enough to support all the equipment and machinery required for hoisting, and the trestles were wide enough to accommodate most of the field offices, work shanties, repair shops and storage sheds. Though the trestles were also wide enough to accommodate small trucks, virtually all heavy equipment and bridge components were delivered to the tower bases by barge.

First step in tower erection was placement of the base plates. Fifteen 6-inch thick slabs, some weighing 27,500 pounds, and all machined to within ten one-thousandths of an inch of their specified dimensions, were set side by side on each pedestal and welded together. These distribute the weight of the tower legs across a wide area of the pedestals and provide a level seat for the first tier section which are held in place by the anchor bolts cast in the concrete.

Both contractors used derrick boats to set the base plates, the first two tiers of steel, and to erect the creeper derricks that were used for the remainder of the tower erection. A creeper is a steel frame that brackets the tower and is held to it by flanged vertical rails. The derrick, mounted on the creeper, has a boom long enough to set all the steel in a section above the creeper. Frames, called catheads, attached to the upper tiers support blocks and tackle that raise the creeper from tier to tier. Power for this and other hoisting operations is provided by engines set on the work platforms.

One of the major problems in tower erection was keeping each section perfectly plumb while it was being set. An out-of-plumb section could not be made to mesh with the many connections on adjacent sections.

The contractor on the Island tower coped with this problem by devising several sets of offset ears—steel lugs—that could be bolted at predetermined locations on various sections to provide perfect balance. The Brooklyn contractor built a compli-

November 13, 1963.
Brooklyn side span. Lifting of 400-ton roadway unit.

cated and efficient clamp that could be adjusted to balance any section from its own connector angles.

Both contractors used pneumatic tools for tightening the 1½ million bolts that locked the sections together as they were raised. For horizontal splices, men worked from temporary platforms; for vertical splices, particularly those on the outside of the legs, men worked from small air-power basket scaffolds.

The tower legs were checked regularly for plumbness but always after midnight, when unequal temperatures could not cause distortion. Any deviations were corrected with steel shims that were set between tiers.

When tower erection was completed, the creepers raised and set on each tower top a double boomed 75 ton stiff-leg derrick. These derricks were used to dismantle the creepers, and to set the tower saddles. While not structural components of the towers, these massive steel castings are seated on the tower tops, and are generally considered to be part of the towers.

A cable saddle can most easily be explained by comparison with a horse's saddle. Although proportions differ, both have the same general shape across the riding surface—a double curve. And functionally, one saddle does for the cable and the tower about the same things as the other does for the horse and the rider. Both distribute a concentrated weight over a wide area, both provide a smooth round riding surface free of sharp angles and cutting projections, and both have troughs to prevent sliding.

In relation to the bridge, the curve and trough of the tower saddle are at right angles to those of the saddle on the horse; this is understandable since the cables, which are the equivalent of the rider's legs, run the length of the bridge rather than straddle it.

There are eight tower cable saddles on the Narrows Bridge, two at the top of each tower leg. Each saddle is about 30½ feet long, 8½ feet wide, 11¼ feet high, and each weighs 178 tons. To facilitate fabrication and erection, each saddle was cast in three pieces, the largest weighing 63 tons. These large

November 21, 1963.
Brooklyn side span. Lifting of 400-ton roadway unit.

sections contained so much metal that after they were cast, they took a week to solidify and cool.

The mounting of these saddles plays a big part in maintaining the plumbness of the towers during construction of the suspended structure. Because the center span of a suspension bridge is longer and therefore heavier than the side spans, erection of the center span causes the tower tops to lean inward towards each other.

There are two principal ways of compensating for this inward movement. In one, the saddles are fixed to the tower tops, the tower tops are pulled apart before they are loaded and tied back, out of plumb by the estimated amount of the ultimate inward tilt. Then as the load is applied the tie backs are loosened to allow the towers to plumb themselves. This method is more common in Europe than in the United States. On the Narrows, however, the towers were built, and left, plumb. It should be noted that when both towers are perfectly plumb their tops are $1\frac{5}{8}$ inches further apart than their bases. The towers are so high and so far apart that compensation for the curvature of the earth surface results in this difference.

The saddles were mounted on rollers, 41 inches shoreward of their ultimate position on a curved roller bed fixed to the tower top. They were held in this position by blocks, shims and hydraulic jacks, which were also fixed to the tower top. As the cables were loaded with deck sections and the weight pulled them downward, the saddles moved channelward, pulling the tower tops towards each other ahead of them.

At five separate times when the inward tilt of the towers was as great as the engineers deemed permissable, the towers were plumbed. To do this the engineers transferred the push of the saddles to hydraulic jacks mounted between the saddle and blocks on the channel side of the tower. They then removed shims, or splints, from the front of the saddles at the channel side leaving room for the towers to be moved shoreward under the saddles.

January 18, 1964.
Erection of floor truss unit, the 31st lift in the center span.

To accomplish this movement, the jacks on the water side of the towers were slowly released while jacks on the shoreward side exerted a horizontal pressure between the saddles and pusher blocks fixed to the shore side of the towers. The extension of the shore-side jacks pushed the towers shoreward until they were plumb, at which time the channel side of the saddles rested firmly against the shims on the outshore side.

January 1964.
Brooklyn approach to bridge,
showing roadway steel erection west of the anchorage.

7

One of the most complex, most dangerous, and most romantic phases of the construction of any suspension bridge is the spinning of the great cables that drape over the towers and stretch from anchorage to anchorage to carry the bridgedeck. On the Verrazano Narrows Bridge the cable spinning was particularly awe-inspiring; and at 56.9 million dollars it was also the most expensive single job on the bridge.

There are four cables, two on each side of the bridge and, their total weight is 39,192 tons. Each of these cables is 35⅞ inches in diameter, and is 7,205 feet long. Each is made up of 26,108 wires that were carried across the bay eight at a time, but as separate wires, and each of these wires was laid in its proper place, at exactly its predetermined drape, and each was tensioned individually to maintain that drape.

Yet for all the magnitude and complexity of the cable

February 7, 1964.
Concreting operations near the top of the Brooklyn anchorage.

70

spinning, the operation involves at least three noteworthy paradoxes. First in spite of its complexity and requirements for almost laboratory precision, the basics of cable spinning have changed little since they were developed by John Roebling a century ago. Second, there is no spinning involved in the cable spinning operation; the wires are not interwoven or braided, but are simply carried from anchorage to anchorage on a wheel that lays them side by side and one above the other. Third, the finished "cable" is not a cable as most people visualize one. There are no twisted wires, no spiraling strands, no separate cores, simply a great cylindrical bundle of parallel wires.

Preparation for cable spinning started long before the first wire was carried across the bay—three years before, in fact, when the contractor began making the galvanized wire at his New Jersey plant. The wire was originally stored in thousands of coils each containing about 10,000 feet. The wire in every coil was tested for size, finish and metallic content. Every tenth coil was tested for strength and, while the main cables were designed to be stressed up to only 87,000 pounds per square inch, tests showed that the wire in them was actually capable of sustaining a minimum of 220,000 pounds per square inch and an average of 234,000 psi. Later the coils were joined with tiny but strong turnbuckle type fittings, and rolled onto steel spools each containing about 90 miles of wire and each weighing about 24 tons. In all, 160 reels were made for the job, and each was used about ten times.

Before any actual cable spinning could be done, the contractor had to erect footbridges called catwalks on which the men could stand while working on the cables. There were two such catwalks, one for each pair of cables. Each of these catwalks was itself a suspension bridge, only 20 feet wide, but just as long as the spans that would make up the completed bridge. These catwalks extend from both anchorages to the corresponding towers and between the towers. To support these catwalks the contractor erected temporary frames on the anchorages and the towers and made them adjustable so that the catwalks could be kept three feet below the bottom of the cable even as the

March 13, 1964.
Four-hundred-ton center span roadway
unit near Brooklyn tower.

cable sagged under its own weight and the weight of the suspended span.

Each catwalk was supported by 12 wire ropes. In order to construct the center span catwalk across the Narrows, each rope was wound on a reel rack which in turn was set on a barge. The barge was towed to a tower base where the free end of the rope was connected to a line from a derrick at the top of that tower. The barge was then towed to the base of the other tower where the other end of the rope was similarly connected to another derrick. On a given signal, both derricks lifted the rope ends so that they could be connected, with the proper drape, to the catwalk frames.

Raising the catwalk ropes for the sidespans had to be handled differently since both sidespans are partly over land. On the Brooklyn side, the contractor built a temporary bridge over the parkway that runs between the anchorage and the tower. A barge carrying the rope (again on a reel) came as close inshore as possible, and the free end of the rope was hooked onto a line from a winch set up on the anchorage. The winch then pulled the line from the reel across the bridge on dollies. After the free end of the rope was connected to the catwalk frame on the anchorage, the other end was lifted to the top of the tower by the tower derrick, just as the mainspan ropes were. On the Staten Island side, with no highway to contend with, the job was simpler but similar.

Throughout the entire raising of the catwalk ropes their weight was balanced so that there was almost no bending of the towers because of an excessive pull in either direction by the ropes.

The walkway of the catwalk consisted of chain link fencing stapled to wooden crossbeams. This was made up ahead of time to its full 20 foot width in 100 foot lengths and shipped to the job in bundles that were folded like an accordion. Each bundle was barged to the tower base and lifted by the tower derrick to the underside of the catwalk ropes. The end crossbeam was attached to the ropes by U bolts, and at the outside edges of

March 20, 1964.
Approaching "close in" time on the Brooklyn side span roadway.

74

the crossbeam workers bolted angle iron uprights that would hold the hand ropes. This done, the end crossbeam was allowed to slide down under the catwalk ropes, taking the slack chain link fencing behind it. The process was repeated for each successive crossbeam.

As each 100 foot chain link section slid down the ropes to its full length another section was wired to it, and the process was continued. When the chain link from both towers neared the middle of the main span, the opposing lengths were pulled together by winches so they were taut. While this was being put on the mainspan, similar material was slid down the sidespans towards the anchorages at a sufficient rate to keep an even load on the towers so they would not bend.

In the steeper sections of the catwalk, wood cleats were attached to the upper side of the chain link to provide a foothold for the workmen.

To stabilize the catwalks in the face of wind action, and to reduce bouncing under moving loads, such as a man running on them, or spot sagging under concentrated loads, such as a group of men working at one point, guy wires were run from the base of the towers to various points on the catwalks. In addition, the two catwalks were joined at about 500 feet intervals by light, but rigid cross struts. Three of these cross struts in the main span were light truss footbridges that permitted workmen to cross from one catwalk to the other without going back to the towers.

As an added precaution chicken wire was attached to both outside edges of the chain link in order to keep men from sliding over the edge. Tragically enough, one of the three deaths that occurred during the construction of the Narrows Bridge resulted from the temporary removal of one small section of this chicken wire. A man jumped from the north cable to the catwalk at about midpoint on the Brooklyn sidespan, slipped through the opening, and fell to his death in the water. In addition, one man fell to his death inside the Brooklyn tower and another died in a fall from one of the Brooklyn approach structures.

1964.
Lifting attachment being connected to the
"last key unit." Brooklyn side, looking west.

During construction of the catwalks, the contractor set up the equipment for spinning the cables. Mainly this comprised two reel stands, four tensioning towers, four haul ropes, two haul rope engines and eight double-sheaved spinning wheels.

The spinning wheels, each mounted on a V-shaped frame were clamped at opposite ends of each haul rope in such a way that, as they moved across the bridge, they would pass each other at the exact center of the main span. Each of the spinning wheels was equipped with a headlight so that it could be seen at night and a cowbell so that it could be heard night or day.

At the start of the cable spinning, workers at one anchorage pulled the ends of wire from two reels through the upper sheaves on the tensioning tower then looped the wires under counterweighted sheaves within the tower. These counter-weight sheaves are not on fixed shafts; in fact, they are actually supported by the individual wires somewhat as a yo-yo is supported by its string, and like a yo-yo these sheaves move up and down within the towers to maintain a constant tension of the wires regardless of their speed.

The ends of the wires were reeved through other sheaves and through the splay saddles on the anchorage and tied to the catwalk. The wires were then looped over the strand shoes at either side of an eye-bar chain and over the sheaves of the spinning wheel.

At a signal, the engines started moving the hauling rope. The two spinning wheels, one at each anchorage, began climbing upward towards the towers, each other, and finally the opposite anchorage. Each carried two loops that would roll out as four wires. The bottom of each loop, fixed at its end to the catwalk, did not move but merely rolled off the wheel as it sped across the spans. This was called the dead wire. The top of the loop running back to the reel, had to move so the wheel could extend the loop. This was called the live wire.

As the wheels passed over each tower, and at stations on the

April 15, 1964.
Looking across Brooklyn side span, lower deck.

78

main span, the dead wires were set directly on the cable saddles, the live wires were set on free turning sheaves.

Throughout the trip of the wheel, men on the mainspan were checking the drape of the dead wire against that established by a previously set guide wire. They telephoned instructions to the towers, or the anchorages, as the case might be, where other men were equipped to tighten the wires with clamps and electric winches.

When each wheel reached the anchorage opposite that from which it had started, its wires were removed, looped over their respective strand shoes and remounted on the wheel for the return trip. At this point the wires that had been alive now became dead, and they too were adjusted.

To simplify the spinning operation each cable was placed as 61 strands, each containing 428 wires.

The first four wires placed during the first trip of one spinning wheel were placed in strand No. 1. The four wires carried at the same time by the other wheel from the opposite anchorage became part of strand No. 2. On the return trip wheel No. 1 carried wires for strand No. 3, and wheel No. 2 carried wires for strand No. 4. This alternating of strands allowed men on the catwalks, the towers, and the anchorages to adjust individual wires without stopping the wheels.

If, in spite of adjustment, a wire was too long, and therefore draped too low, it was cut and shortened by a predetermined amount. If a wire was too short(and therefore too high) it was cut and lengthened by inclusion of a short piece of wire. Naturally, the cut ends were spliced together.

Throughout the entire spinning operation the workmen were very careful to keep each wire in its own line, free of twists, kinks and entanglements with other wires. To make certain that the wires of various strands would stay in their proper places workmen tied them together from time to time.

When four strands of one cable were completed, the contractor had what he called a "set-up." Working on one strand at a time, the men removed all temporary ties, shook out the

May 4, 1964.
Erection of the last section of floor steel between the towers.

wires and again made certain that none were crossed or twisted. Then, using small hand tools they banded the wires of the strand together at ten foot intervals to form a circle about 4½ inches in diameter.

After each strand was banded its drape was readjusted by the placing or removing of shims in the linkage of the eye bar chains. So delicate was this operation that all measurements on the strands were taken after midnight, when all the wires in the strands were close to the same temperature, and therefore the same length as possible. While the strands in one cable were being adjusted, men were starting the spinning of four more strands in the adjacent cable.

The cable spinning was started on March 4, 1963 and was completed on August 22nd. Work was done by about 600 men on 7½ hour shifts each day, five days a week. The first two shifts spun wires, the third banded and adjusted the wire and made minor repairs. Major repairs, except in case of break-downs, were made on weekends.

Completion of cable spinning did not complete the cables. The strands still had to be pressed into a cylindrical shape, cable bands had to be placed at intervals, and the cables between them had to be wrapped with a tight, continuous spiral of steel wire.

To press the wires into shape the contractor used eight compactors. These were hexagonal steel frames carrying radially like the spokes of a wheel, six hydraulic jacks, each capable of exerting an inward pressure of 300 tons. The frames were in two pieces so they could be put around the cable, then be bolted together. The jacks carried interlocking shoes that were of the right size and shape for forming the cable. As the jacks squeezed the wires together at 3 foot intervals the wires were wrapped with steel bands so they would hold their shape.

When the cables were compacted, the workmen then draped rubber covered steel slings over them and connected these slings to the crossbeams of the catwalks. They then removed the wire ropes that had previously supported the catwalks and left the catwalks hanging directly from the cables. The ropes were returned to the factory where they had been made. Here they were inspected and cut into predetermined lengths so they could be used as suspender ropes in the finished bridge. The ends of each length were socketed—that is, fitted with a heavy forged steel cylinder which ultimately would support part of the suspended structure—and the ropes were then returned to the bridge site.

Meanwhile, at the site, workmen were placing and tightening cable bands around the cables. The cable bands, each a pair of matched half-cylinders put around a cable and bolted together, serve three purposes; they hold the cable wires together, they support the suspender ropes, and they distribute the weight of the suspended structure over a wide area of the cables.

They vary in weight from 2,562 to 6,307 pounds, and in length from 2 feet to 6 feet. The reason for the variance in weight and length is that in the almost horizontal section of the cable—such as at the center of the main span—a short band can rest easily with no danger of slipping. Where the angle of the cable is steeper, such as in the main span near the tower, and in the side spans, gravity and the weight of the suspended structure tend to pull bands downhill. In these sections of the cable, the bands must be long enough to provide a gripping surface sufficient to counteract these forces. The bands were carried to their respective positions by small but sturdy frames that straddled a pair of cables, and rode them on four wooden wheels curved to conform to their circular shape.

8

Late in October of 1963 the first deck section of the Narrows Bridge was lifted from a barge and raised more than 200 feet into the air to be suspended beneath the main cables of the structure. Regardless of the cost, complexity, massiveness, height or beauty of all the rest of the structure, only the deck is functional from the standpoint of carrying traffic.

The deck, although it was the last of the major components to be built, was among the first to be considered, even when the bridge was in its preliminary design stages. This had to be, for the diameter of the cables, the size of the towers, the area of the foundations, and the weight of the anchorages, were all determined to a large extent by the requirements of the roadway. The design of the suspended structure was developed from many studies of traffic flow, economic considerations and engineering criteria.

June 13, 1964.
Erection of "intermediate" steel.

The number of lanes was determined by estimates of the number of vehicles the bridge would carry—12.6 million the first year; later as many as 48 million annually. The arrangement of the lanes was based on both economic and engineering considerations. Economic studies revealed that an 8 lane, single deck bridge would cost about $20 million per lane, while a double-deck bridge with six lanes on each deck could be built with an increase of only 10% in the cost of the entire structure. Obviously the 10% increase in cost would be a bargain since it would increase the capacity of the bridge enormously and in doing so, permit it to meet traffic requirements for many years to come.

One of the main engineering factors had to do with wind, for in spite of their great weight, the decks of suspension bridges (and also other types of bridges) can be deflected and distorted by wind if they are not rigid enough. An undulating motion is set up which may tear apart the deck.

The collapse in 1941 of the unfortunate "Galloping Gertie" over the Tacoma Narrows in the State of Washington was mainly due to these undulations, which increase by their own effect. Its long slender deck was just not rigid enough.

The most effective way to make the deck of a suspension bridge rigid against wind is by including in its design adequate vertical stiffening trusses combined with lateral trusses in two separate planes. A truss is composed of a series of steel members set in the form of adjacent and interrelated triangles or polygons. Whereas the ability of any other polygon to hold its shape depends almost entirely on the rigidity of the connections between the members, a triangle will hold its shape even if the connections between its sides are hinges.

John A. Roebling stiffened the Brooklyn Bridge by shallow stiffening trusses supplemented by diagonal ropes in the suspension system. After Roebling, American engineers relied for many years on stiffening trusses as an integral part of a suspension bridge. Ofter, however, their depth and weight was made far greater than necessary, as notably exemplified in the Williamsburg Bridge in New York.

June 29, 1964.
View from the top of the Staten Island tower toward Brooklyn.
Main span steel erection has been completed and
roadway is being prepared for concreting.

Subsequently engineers began to use shallower, more elegant looking, trusses until in the 1930's several suspension bridges were stiffened by relatively shallow, but aerodynamically very unfavorable solid plate girders in place of trusses. The Tacoma Narrows Bridge was an extreme case of this kind. After its collapse some other suspension bridges which had stood for a short time had to be stiffened. Among these were two Thousand Islands bridges over the Saint Lawrence River, the Deer Isle Bridge in Maine, the Bronx-Whitestone Bridge in New York, and the Golden Gate Bridge in San Francisco.

Owing solely to its exceptionally great weight the George Washington Bridge performed well without stiffening trusses from its completion with single deck in 1931 until erection of its lower deck with stiffening trusses in 1962. The mainspan of the George Washington Bridge is 760 feet shorter than that of the Verrazano-Narrows Bridge, but with 14 lanes for vehicular traffic it is one of the heaviest and most massive suspension bridges ever built.

Thus, from an engineering standpoint, double decking of the Narrows Bridge, in addition to providing much-needed traffic lanes, would also provide the depth of deck needed for adequate rigidity.

The structure suspended from the towers of the Narrows Bridge weighs an average of 37,000 pounds per foot of bridge, somewhat less than that of the George Washington Bridge.

Improvements in design account for much of the weight reduction, but also the designers took advantage of improvements in materials, such as higher strength steels.

Basically the framework of the deck structure forms an open elongated box 115 feet wide and 27 feet deep. The transverse members are rigid rectangular floor frames which carry the roadway decks and add to the torsional rigidity of the deck structure. These floor frames are spaced about 50 feet apart along the full length of the bridge.

They are connected to the main cables by the suspender ropes in a manner that may be likened to that used in hooking

July 8, 1964.
Steel erection completed for upper and lower deck.

88

up a child's swing. Both the seat of the swing and the floor truss are held up by a "knot" at the bottom of the rope that is too big to pull through the hole above it. In the case of the swing, the rope is slid through the hole in the seat and then the knot is tied. For the floor frame the "knot," in the form of a forged socket, is firmly attached to the suspender rope before the rope is slid into the frame. To make it hold, one side of each hole in the frame is larger than the socket, the other side is smaller. The socket is slid through the enlarged part of the hole, and then the cable and its socket are slid sideways into the smaller part and held in place by a device called a keeper.

On each side each floor frame is connected to the vertical stiffening trusses; on top and bottom each is connected to the horizontal wind trusses.

In building short or low bridges with simple decks, it is usually fast, safe and economical to put the individual deck members directly into place one at a time. In building a structure as high, wide, and long as that of the Narrows deck, this procedure would take too much time, would cost too much money, and would add more hazards to an already hazardous job.

Consequently, only four short sections of the steel deck structure, one at each side of each tower, were assembled in place. The remainder of the suspended structure was designed as 71 separate units which could be assembled mostly on the ground, where men could work safely and quickly on assembly line-like procedures.

The company established three assembly sites. Two of these, which were relatively small, were near the anchorage on each side of the Bay. The yard in Brooklyn was used for the assembly of the four sections of the suspended structure that are over land on that side; the yard in Staten Island for the seven sections of the structure that are over land there.

The main assembly area was a 22 acre waterfront railroad yard in Jersey City, about five miles from the bridge. Here

July 16, 1964.
The nearly completed structure from the Brooklyn shore.

the entire over-water section of the suspended structure was assembled.

To these yards, on a carefully planned schedule, came small pieces of the deck that were fabricated in plants in New York, New Jersey, Pennsylvania and Virginia. These small pieces were first put together as minor sub-assemblies. The sub-assemblies were grouped to make major sub-assemblies which in turn were assembled to form the 400 ton floor truss lifting sections that were the basic units of the field construction.

A typical lifting section consists of two floor frames joined together by almost all of the horizontal, vertical and diagonal steel that is included in the finished structure. Specifically this includes 2 bottom stiffening trusses, 2 top stiffening trusses, 4 laterals, 8 diagonals, and 16 "stringers," or floor beams. It also includes 4 brackets (nicknamed pork chops because of their shape) which form extensions of the transverse frames.

In the Jersey City yard, the contractor built a 900 foot long railroad track on top of an absolutely level concrete foundation. The floor sections were assembled on dollies riding on this track. As each was finished, it was rolled out on to a trestle over the water. At low tide a barge was floated under the trestle and heavy blocks were set on its deck at predetermined points of support. As the tide rose, so did the barge until the blocks contacted the section, and lifted it off the tracks. The barge was then towed five miles to the site of the bridge, and the section was lifted off and raised into place.

The mechanism for lifting the heavy floor truss sections consisted mainly of four powerful, four-drum hoists, set in pairs on the lower transverse strut of each tower, and 16 small four-wheeled carriages called lifting struts. From a distance they resembled railroad handcars, but while handcars ride on tracks, the lifting struts rode on the bridge cables.

When being moved from place to place, each strut rolled on small concaved wooden wheels, curved to fit snugly over the round upper surface of the cables so as not to damage cable wires. When the struts were actually being used for lifting a section, their wheels were blocked up and the struts were firmly clamped to the cables so they could not move.

The lifting struts were used in groups of four, one for each corner of the section being raised. There were four on each side span and eight on the main span, four on each side of the center.

These lifting struts were positioned directly over the ultimate position of the respective floor truss sections and the lines from the struts were run diagonally back toward the towers so they could be hooked on to the out-of-position units. Each of these units was tied back to the tower base and as it was raised, the lines to the tower base were slacked off permitting the unit to move away diagonally from the tower towards its final location.

In figuring out the sequence of erection for the floor truss units the engineers had to consider three major effects of the increasing weight on the cables: changes in the curvature of the cables, the tipping inward of the towers, and the overall lengthening of the cables under the weight.

As incongruous as it may seem, these problems can best be illustrated by comparing the towers and the cables with a pair of slender, flexible poles supporting a slack wash line that is used for airing heavy winter clothes. If a clothes hanger carrying a heavy jacket is hung on the line, the line will sag to the point where the hanger is hooked. The natural curvature of the line will change, and in fact will tend to straighten out between the hanger and each poles. If the poles are flexible enough they will tilt inward towards each other as more and more weight is placed on the line. At the same time, the ever-increasing weight will stretch the line so that even if the poles were to remain plumb or be made plumb, the center of the line would be lower under the load than it would without it.

This is just about what happens to the towers and cables of a suspension bridge as the deck is added. However, where the drape of a clothes line is of little consequence, the curve of a bridge cable is vital. Therefore the engineers had to prescribe an erection sequence that would accomplish three things: distort the cables as little as possible, keep the towers as plumb as possible and stretch the cables in such a way that the joint of each section would line up those of the preceding sections.

On virtually every suspension bridge previously built in the United States, the contractors started deck erection at both towers and simultaneously worked outward in both directions towards midspan and towards the anchorages. On the Narrows Bridge, however, the engineers decided to follow a procedure quite common in Europe: to start at the center of the mainspan and work towards the towers, adding sections to the sidespans as needed for counterbalance.

Because of the "reverse construction" the first section raised was the keystone piece. (The name is a carryover from arch bridge construction, where the center piece, always the last one placed, became the key stone in that it completes the arch and permits the two sides to stand without external supports.)

The keystone piece at the Narrows was one of the smallest and lightest of the floor sections. It contained only a single floor truss. Still, it was 115 feet wide, 27½ feet deep and 76 feet long. It weighed 172 tons and this weight pulled the center of the main cables down a full 20 inches.

The second and third units, raised adjacent to either side of the keystone piece, were full floor truss sections, 100 feet long. Each weighed about 400 tons, and in addition, each carried on its top steel a 35 ton truck crane that was later used for erection of "second pass steel"—materials such as filler pieces, roadway deck grid, center barriers, not included in the initial assemblies.

The weight of the second and third sections and their cranes pulled the cables down another 4 feet 6 inches. The fourth and fifth sections added another 4 feet 3 inches to the sag.

Under the full weight of the completed deck, without traffic, the center of the cables is 28 feet lower than its original location. Under the full traffic load at extreme temperatures the

1964.
View from the air, looking north from Lower Bay.

cables can drape as much as 35 feet below their original location.

To counterbalance the weight of the first five sections suspended in the mainspan, the contractor next raised one truss section in each of the side spans. In general, from this point on, the erection procedure followed a similar pattern: for each four sections raised in the main span (two on each side of the center) one section was raised in each of the side spans.

Meanwhile, since the mainspan is almost twice the combined length of the sidespans, the continuing adding of weight to the cables caused the towers to lean inward towards each other a total of over 3½ feet. At no time, though, was the inclination of either tower greater than 3 inches because each time the tilt approached that amount, the towers were plumbed by being jacked shoreward against the cable saddles. The towers were plumbed five times during construction, the last time after virtually all other work on the bridge was finished.

In spite of this partially balanced construction, and the jacking of the towers, it was not possible to connect adjacent sections permanently, as fast as they were raised. The distortion of the cables under the concentrated loads prevented more than a temporary pinning until enough sections were raised to bring the drape of the cables into a shape near that of the final curve. Then the splice plates on adjacent sections began to line up closely enough for the iron workers to connect them with high strength bolts.

As fast as the prefabricated sections aligned themselves the contractor began placing steel members left out during initial assembly. One of the big problems was making sure that no fixed connections were made at points that had to remain flexible to allow for continuing realignment under the increasing loads of the deck sections.

The roadway was the last of the major suspended structure components to be placed. It consists of a grid of steel beams, and reinforcing rods, welded to basic floor members and to each other, and covered by a concrete slab having a total thickness of 6 inches.

The sequence for welding of the grid and placing the concrete was critical on two points: retaining flexibility where needed, and maintaining a balanced load on the cables. While the roadway placement varied somewhat as between the upper and lower decks, and from that originally planned for either, it followed a general pattern. The central section of the main span was placed first, and this was balanced by similar construction in the sidespans and the river side of the towers.

The grid steel was sandblasted before concreted so as to be free of scale and rust. Initially, concrete for the upper roadway was delivered by mixer trucks to the ends of the bridge. Here the material was poured into power buggies, small vehicles resembling golf carts, with a bucket at the front. These travelled on plywood runways to the pouring sites.

Later when the side span concrete was sufficiently hard trucks were allowed to come to the towers to shorten the run of the buggies. Most of the lower deck concrete was loaded into the buggies through chutes from hoppers on the upper deck.

The 960,000 square feet of concrete roadway was placed in 16 weeks and was completed on September 30, 1964.

All other essential miscellaneous work, such the final jacking of the towers, installing of electrical work, painting of the cables, removal of derricks and other equipment—was completed before the scheduled opening of the bridge.

Appendix

The Six Largest U.S. Suspension Bridges

Some Comparative Figures

Item	Unit	Verrazano-Narrows Bridge	Golden Gate Bridge	Mackinac Bridge	George Washington Bridge	Tacoma Narrows Bridge	Oakland Bay Bridge
Length of Main Span	feet	4,260	4,200	3,800	3,500	2,800	2,310
Length of each Side Span	feet	1,215	1,125	1,800	610/650	1,100	1,160
Length of Suspended Structure	feet	6,690	6,450	7,400	4,760	5,000	10,450
Length incl. Approach Struct.	feet	13,700	8,981	19,205	5,800	5,979	43,500
Width of Bridge (C-C Cables)	feet	103	90	68	106	60	66
Number of Traffic Lanes		12	6	4	14	4	9
Height of Towers above MHW	feet	690	746	552	595	500	447
Clearance at center above MHW	feet	228	215	148	220	187	203
Deepest Foundation below MHW	feet	170	115	210	75	224	235
Diameter of Cable	inches	35⅞	36	24½	36	20¼	28¾
Length of one Cable	feet	7,205	7,650	8,683	5,235	5,500	5,080
Number of wires per Cable	ea.	26,108	27,572	12,580	26,474	8,702	17,464
Total length of wire used	miles	142,500	80,000	41,000	105,000	20,000	70,800
Year of Completion		1964	1937	1958	1931	1950	1936

Note: The Oakland Bay Bridge includes two spans end to end; the Verrazano-Narrows and the George Washington bridges are double-decked. Information compiled by Edward M. Young, courtesy of Engineering News-Record.

Narrows Bridge Data

Total length including approach structures........13,900 ft
Length of suspended structure............6,690 ft
Length of main span................4,260 ft
Length of each side span..................1,215 ft
Width of bridge (center to center of cables)........103 ft
Width floor trusses..................115 ft 2 in.
Number of decks................2
Number of traffic lanes..................12
Height of towers above mean high water..............690 ft
Center clearance at mean high water....................228 ft
Min clearance at mean high water..........................216 ft
Deepest foundation below mean high water........170 ft
Number of cables................4
Length of one cable..................7,205 ft
Diameter of cable..................35⅞ in.
Strands per cable................61
Wires per strand..................428
Number of wires per cable....................26,108
Weight of wire in cables................38,500 tons
Total length of wire in cables....................145,000 miles
Structural steel in main bridge....................160,000 tons
Reinforcing steel in main bridge....................28,000 tons
Concrete in main bridge............593,000 cu yd

Cost in millions:
Total (Est.)..................................$324.0
Tower foundations..................$ 16.5
Anchorages ....$ 17.9
Towers ....$ 46.0
Main cables..................$ 56.89
Suspended roadway structure..............$ 36.55

Construction time..............900,000 man days (approx.)

Courtesy of Engineering News-Record

Acknowledgments

The construction of the Verrazano-Narrows Bridge required the combined and coordinated efforts of hundreds of suppliers, dozens of contractors and more than 10,000 men. It would be impractical, if not impossible, to list them all, but certain of the organizations and the men involved must in all fairness be given credit for the roles they played. Exclusion of others is in no way intended to deprecate their contributions to the successful completion of what will undoubtedly remain for decades to come one of the greatest engineering and construction feats of all time.

Among those deserving of special note are:

Triborough Bridge and Tunnel Authority   *Owner*
    Robert Moses   Chairman
    George E. Spargo   General Manager (to 1963)
    Peter Reidy   Executive Director
    Arthur S. Hodgkiss   Deputy Executive Director
    Joseph F. Vermaelen   Director, Construction and Maintenance

Ammann & Whitney   *Consulting Engineers*
   Othmar H. Ammann   Partner
   Milton Brumer   Partner
   Nomer Gray   Partner
   John W. Kinney   Engineer of Construction
   H. G. Decancq   Resident Engineer

Steers-Snare   *Tower Foundations*
   J. Rich Steers, Inc., N.Y.
   Frederick Snare Corp. N.Y.
   Earl Larsen   Project Manager

Johnson-Kiewit   *Anchorages*
   Arthur A. Johnson Corp. N.Y.
   Peter Kiewit Son's Co. Omaha
   Henry Schmekpeper   Project Manager, Brooklyn
   Neil Friets   Project Manager, Staten Island

Bethlehem Steel Company   *Staten Island Tower*
   A. C. Spallitta   Project Manager
   C. E. Adams   Superintendent

Harris Structural Steel Company   *Brooklyn Tower*
   John Schnier   Project Manager
   F. H. Horton   Superintendent

American Bridge Division of U.S. Steel Corp.   *Cable Work*
   D. B. Rees   Project Manager   *and Sus-*
   J. R. Murphy   General Superintendent   *pended*
   J. H. Kelly   Superintendent   *Structure*

The artist and author are deeply indebted to Messrs. Robert Moses, Othmar H. Ammann, and John W. Kinney. Special thanks are due to Mr. Joseph Vermaelen for permission to go upon the Narrows Bridge and its approaches in order to record, in pen and ink and the printed word, its construction from start to finish, and to Mr. H. George Decancq for clarifying construction procedure and for supplying the captions for the original artwork.